the Twelve Voices of Christmas

by Woodrow Kroll

BACK TO THE BIBLE
Lincoln, Nebraska 68501

8,000 printed to date—1993
(5-8959-8M-113)
ISBN 0-8474-1456-6

Printed in the United States of America.

CONTENTS

Zacharias

VOICE OF DISBELIEF
Luke 1:5-25, 57-80

*Y*ou will have a son," the angel told Zacharias. Startled by this message, he saw his life opened, exposed. Outer layers of devotion, service and submission were torn back, laying bare a root of bitterness and disbelief. But God took that discordant response to His message of Christmas and changed it into a song of praise.

I had three great loves in my life. Above all, I loved the Lord. I worshiped and served Him as faithfully as I knew how.

My second love was Elizabeth, my wife. We stood together in our faith, and we wanted to please God in everything we did.

My third love was my work. I was a priest, as was my father. I grew up in the temple precincts. Serving as a priest was all I ever wanted to do; and in spite of the spiritual decadence of many of the priests I worked with, I found my service stimulating and rewarding.

There could have been a fourth love—if only God had given us a child. Elizabeth and I had prayed for a son every day for years, but she was barren. Now we were well beyond the age for having children. It was too late.

In addition to having a son, there was one another thing I wanted very much. I wanted to burn the incense, the offering on

the golden altar in the Holy Place. What a privilege that would be—an opportunity never to be repeated in the lifetime of a priest! Every time lots were cast, I prayed that I might be chosen.

And then, one day, the lot fell to me.

As I entered the Holy Place that day, I focused my attention on the ceremony I was to perform and the prayer I was to offer on behalf of my people. The other priests worshiped and then withdrew from the room. Finally, I was alone. It was the most solemn moment of my life.

I could see the altar of incense only by the light of the seven-branched candlestick. When I placed the incense over the red coals on the altar, a cloud of smoke arose. Its fragrance permeated the sanctuary.

I was just about to worship and withdraw, when I realized that I was not alone. Someone was standing next to the altar—an angel.

I was terrified!

"Don't be afraid," he told me. "Your prayers have been heard. Your wife, Elizabeth, will bear a son, and you will name him John. He will be filled with the Holy Spirit, even from his mother's womb. He will preach in the spirit and power of Elijah. And he will prepare the hearts of the people for the Messiah."

Instantly, something welled up from the depths of my heart—rebellion I didn't even know was there. No, I told myself, *it cannot be true.*

"I'm an old man," I said. "My wife is an old woman. People as old as we are don't become parents."

His response was immediate. "I am Gabriel, who stands in the presence of God. And I was sent to bring you this good news."

Gabriel's reply devastated me. How could I utter my feeble contradictions when God had spoken?

Why had I mistrusted him? He was obviously an angel. Why had I rejected what he said? Had I harbored bitterness against God all these years, thinking He had ignored my prayers? Had I covered disbelief with a layer of submission, not recognizing my sin?

If only I had been quiet and spent more time thinking instead of talking, I might have remembered that God made a similar promise to Abraham concerning a son to be born, and it came true.

I then asked for a sign. "How shall I know this will happen?" The angel gave me one, but it wasn't the kind of sign I had in mind. God would take away my ability to speak until after my son was born,

because I had not believed the angel's message.

Meanwhile, the people in the outer court, who had been praying, began to wonder what had happened to me. They had seen the smoke of the burning incense rise from the Holy Place. Why hadn't I come out to give the benediction? Had something gone wrong?

When at last I appeared, I motioned to them, trying to tell them what had happened. But there was no way I could communicate, and they assumed that I had seen a vision.

On the greatest day of my life, the day I served in the temple, the day I learned that God would give me a son—I couldn't tell my good news to anyone.

When I completed my duties at the temple, I returned home. I had so much to tell Elizabeth, but I couldn't speak. Laboriously, I wrote out everything that happened. She was astonished and happy when she read about the son whom God had promised. She cried when she read my confession of disbelief. I cried, too, confessing my sin and turning to God in repentance.

Elizabeth became pregnant soon after that. We carried our treasured secret through days and months of silence. People knew that something had happened in the temple, but they weren't sure what. We didn't tell them. Finally, it became evident that she was carrying my child.

Elizabeth gave birth to a beautiful baby boy, just as the angel had promised. Friends and relatives came from all over to help us celebrate his birth. They were shouting and singing and praising the Lord, and all I could do was watch.

The baby was to be named on the day of his circumcision, when he was eight days old. Everyone assumed we would name him Zacharias, after me. But Elizabeth objected, "Definitely not! We will call him John." Even when our friends objected that we had no relatives by that name, she would not give in.

Then everyone looked at me. "What will you name him?" they asked. I motioned for my writing tablet and wrote, "His name is John."

As our friends and relatives were animatedly discussing the unusual choice of name, suddenly, without warning, I was able to speak.

Immediately I was filled with the Holy Spirit, and I began to prophesy and sing a song of praise to the Lord. "Blessed is the Lord God of Israel, for He has visited and redeemed His people, and has raised up a horn of salvation for us in the house of His servant David."

There was more to this song, much more about the Lord and about our son. John would be a prophet of the Most High, and he would give knowledge of salvation to his people.

During those silent months, the seeds of some of these ideas had germinated in my mind, and they had been watered through hours of meditation. No longer did I doubt. God had silenced my voice of disbelief forever. The Messiah was coming! How wonderful that God had first announced this within His sanctuary—to me. I gladly take my place as one of the twelve voices of Christmas.

Mary

VOICE OF WONDER
Luke 1:26-38

No other person was more astonished at the events in her life than was Mary. As the Christmas story unfolded, she was struck with awe. She wondered at the message of the angel, at the words of Elizabeth, at the experience of Zachariah. She wondered at the birth of her baby and the homage paid to Him. But most of all she wondered at the graciousness of God in choosing her to give birth to the Savior of the world.

I was going about my daily routine at my home in Nazareth when I heard a knock at my door. My parents were not home, and I was apprehensive when I saw a stranger standing there. He didn't look familiar at all. Somehow he didn't even look human.

"May I help you, sir?" I asked.

After the customary greeting, he blessed me, saying, "You are a highly favored person. The Lord is with you."

What a strange greeting! I didn't know what it meant. I was nobody special. My family was not special; we were poor, ordinary people. We lived in Nazareth, not Jerusalem. Everyone from Nazareth was considered to be less than middle class. How could I be a highly favored one? I was bewildered and even upset.

"Do not be afraid, Mary," he said, "for you have found favor with God." It was then that I realized he was no ordinary man. He must be a messenger from God, although I could hardly comprehend it. Later I learned that he was Gabriel, an angel sent from the throne room of God.

Then he told me how God would favor me. I would conceive and bear a Son. *That just isn't possible,* I thought. *I can't have a baby. I'm a virgin. How can that be?*

The messenger continued, "You will name Him Jesus. He will be great, and will be called the Son of the highest. God will give Him the throne of His father David, and He will reign over the house of Jacob forever. His kingdom will never end."

I asked the angel, "How can this possibly be, since I'm a virgin?" It wasn't that I didn't believe it. I believed everything he had told me, no matter how incomprehensible. I just didn't understand it. How could such a wonderful thing take place?

Then Gabriel explained how all this would happen. He said the Holy Spirit would come over me in such a way that the power of God would enclose me; and in the shadow of His overarching Shekinah glory, I would become pregnant. My holy child would not be the offspring of Joseph. He would be the Son of God!

The birth of Isaac to Abraham and Sarah in their old age was miraculous. But the birth of my baby would be more than miraculous; it would be unique. He would be born to me, a virgin, conceived without the benefit of a father. He would be human *and* divine. He would be the Son of God *and* the Son of a humble Nazarene girl.

Then the messenger said, "Nothing will be impossible with God." I believed him.

I knew becoming pregnant before I was married would endanger my relationship with Joseph and put my reputation at stake. But I was willing to face the shame and reproach, for I knew that God's supernatural hand was at work within me. Humbly I gave my assent. I said, "God, whatever you want, I want."

Everything Gabriel announced to me came true. I eventually did marry Joseph, although our marriage was not consummated until after Jesus was born.

When the time for my delivery was approaching, Joseph had a difficult decision to make. A census was to be taken, and each man had to go to the city of his ancestors to enroll his household. For Joseph, that was Bethlehem, the City of David. Should he leave me at home in Nazareth? I might be treated rudely, for everyone knew I was pregnant before my marriage. Should he take me along? It would be a difficult trip for a pregnant woman, involving days of grueling travel. But I longed to see Bethlehem again, so Joseph decided to take me with him.

During that exhausting trip, I had time to ponder many things, including the words of Micah, which one of the rabbis had told us about. The Messiah would be born in Bethlehem, he had said. So even though this census was ordered by a ruler who wanted to add to his own glory, he was unknowingly making it possible for Micah's prophecy to be fulfilled.

We arrived in Bethlehem late one afternoon. The town was swarming with people there for the enrollment. I was very tired, but there was no place to stay—the inns were full. People saw me and then quickly looked away. My situation was obvious, but no one cared to give up his bed for me. I did not tell Joseph, but I was feeling an occasional light pain. The labor was beginning. At last Joseph returned with the news that he had found a place to stay. It was only a stable, but it would be warm and away from the eyes and ears of curious people.

I gave birth to Jesus during the night. We wrapped Him in what we had—long strips of cloth—and laid Him in a manger. There wasn't much light, only a small oil lamp. But I could see the features of His tiny face, and I cried. Everything came back to me—the words of the angel, the inspired words of Elizabeth, the message of the angel to Zachariah. I thought of dear Joseph and his firm faith in what the angel had told him. I remembered his tender care for me throughout my pregnancy. And I looked at that baby in wonder.

Later that night, while I was cuddling Jesus in my arms, some shepherds appeared. They wanted to see the baby. They, too, had been visited by an angel—in fact, a whole host of angels. That is how they had heard that Jesus had been born. When they left the stable that night, they were glorifying God and praising Him for all they had seen and heard, determined to tell everyone their story. But I remained silent as I thought about all that had happened.

Looking back now, I still don't understand everything. I've often thought of Eve, in the Garden of Eden. By her, sin and death were brought into the world. But by the birth of my Son, life and immortality were made possible.

I thank Jehovah for allowing me to be one of the twelve voices of Christmas. But more importantly, I thank Him for His graciousness in choosing me to be the one through whom His Son came into the world.

Elizabeth

Voice of Blessing
Luke 1:5-25, 57-80

ELIZABETH, VOICE OF BLESSING

*E*lizabeth had experienced God's blessing. He had taken away the reproach of her childlessness. He had signaled the presence of her Messiah through the joyful leap of the baby in her womb. In response, she pronounced a blessing that would extend beyond Mary, who stood before her. It would encompass the nation of Israel and eventually the whole world.

My husband, Zacharias, and I met one day when we were young, and we fell in love. I was the daughter of a priest, and he was a priest also, so our families and friends considered ours to be an excellent match. But more important than that, we knew in our hearts that we were right for each other. We said our vows and embarked on life together.

We built our marriage on one thing—loving God, serving Him and doing whatever He commanded. We stood almost alone in our way of life in our village and the surrounding area. Few others were interested in devoting themselves to God. They thought it was too burdensome to try to keep the laws handed down from Moses. But we found joy in obeying God.

There was only one thing marring our happiness: We wanted a child, but I was barren.

Every Jewish family wanted a baby to hold and care for, a toddler to train, a growing child to guide toward maturity. Every Jewish family wanted a child who would blossom into full maturity and independence, becoming a stabilizing force in the family and a hope for the future. And beyond all this there was the underlying hope that maybe, just maybe, the promised Messiah would be born to that family.

My youth passed quickly, with no baby. What had been a cloud over my life became a heavy sorrow. I never spoke about it to my friends, and they said nothing either; but I know they pitied me.

I would often lie awake at night thinking of Rachel, imagining her saying to Jacob, "Give me children, or else I die." I cried for her. I often thought of Hannah, grieving because she had no children. In my imagination I saw her stricken face as Peninnah, her husband's other wife, ridiculed her.

God heard Hannah's prayer and gave her a son. Why hadn't He heard mine? I had prayed so fervently, so intensely, for so many years.

Again and again I asked Him why. I tried to do all He asked of me. Hadn't it been said that if we obeyed Him, He would give us children? Hadn't God promised our people that we would be blessed above all peoples, that there would not be a male or female barren among us? Didn't He care? Or was there something wrong with me?

As the years went by, hope faded and was finally gone. We no longer spoke of the baby we had wanted so much. But I continued to express our pain in my prayers. I determined that I would not become bitter but would continue to serve God faithfully.

One day, while Zacharias was offering the incense to the Lord in the Holy Place, he was startled by the appearance of the angel Gabriel. His news was even more astonishing. I would give birth to a child, a son, whom we were to name John.

He would be great in the sight of the Lord and many would rejoice at his birth. He would prepare the way for the Messiah, and he would turn many of our people back to God.

I can only imagine the excitement and awe Zacharias must have felt when Gabriel broke this news to him. Yet when he came home, he couldn't tell me about it—he was literally speechless. He wrote down what had happened. "I didn't believe what the angel told me," he wrote. "And this is my punishment."

Zacharias was so ashamed. But I loved him nonetheless, and he loved me. As a result of that love, I conceived.

I had no one else to talk to. Who would have believed me if I had told them what an angel had told Zacharias—that I would bear a special son? Who would have believed that at my advanced age I was pregnant? No one. My neighbors knew I was barren. I couldn't face them for perhaps five months—not until my pregnancy was obvious, not until I could show them that my reproach was gone.

Like Zacharias, I would be silent and alone. How wonderful it would be to meditate on the words the angel had spoken to Zacharias, to think about the son we would have, to glorify God for the miracle of his promised birth. And I would still have time to think about the Messiah, my Lord, who evidently would appear soon—if my son were to prepare the way for Him.

In the sixth month of my pregnancy, Mary arrived from Nazareth. I hadn't expected her visit, but I was very pleased to see her.

When I heard her voice , something strange happened. I felt my baby leap within me. I had felt the baby moving for some time, but never anything like this.

Immediately, I knew that Mary was the chosen mother of the Messiah and that even now she was pregnant with Him. Only the Spirit of God could have revealed that to me.

And He gave me words of blessing to speak that I had never planned to say: "O, Mary, you are so blessed among women, and so is the fruit of your womb. How is it that the mother of my Lord should come to me?"

I felt inspired, transformed. Even as I was blessing Mary for her willingness to believe what the angel had told her, somehow my unborn son was offering homage to his Lord. Yet all the time, in the back of my mind I felt compassion for Zacharias, who had not believed.

After my blessing, Mary responded with a song of praise to God, for His blessing on her, on Israel and on the world through His Son.

That day we laughed and cried together. She told me what Gabriel had told her, and I repeated to her what he had told Zacharias. Each message confirmed the truth of the other. We talked and talked.

For three months we shared our feelings, our joys, our hopes, our concerns and anticipations. Our futures held many questions, but our joy was infectious. Then Mary returned home to face Joseph with the news of her pregnancy. And I faced childbirth.

I remember how I felt as she left. I was so happy. I loved my husband. I loved my baby, and I loved Mary. Both she and I were greatly blessed to be voices of the Christmas story. She was carrying the Messiah, the Savior of the world. And I was carrying His forerunner, the one who would prepare the way for Him.

Joseph

VOICE OF REASON
Matthew 1:16-25

There was no music in Joseph's soul. Mary, his fiancee, was pregnant, and the child was not his. Being a man of reason, He considered his alternatives carefully and made his decision. But reason did not reign that day—God did. And the angel's message to him made his heart sing.

As a child, I watched my father's strong and skillful hands turn pieces of wood into beautiful furniture. How I wanted to be a good carpenter like him.

I watched him carefully and listened to what he said, as every child watches and listens—and judges—a parent. I saw that he was generous, kind, loving, honest and wise. But above all, I noticed his deep love for God. He was everything I wanted to be.

As a young man, I began to think of having a family of my own, one in which I could be the kind of leader that my father was. It was Jewish custom for families to arrange marriages. The first son of Jacob—me—would marry the first daughter of Eli. Her name was Mary. She was much too young to be married, but I watched her from a distance, and I loved her.

While I watched her mature, I honed my skills as a craftsman, for I wanted to be ready to support a wife and any children God might send us. And I studied the Law of God and prayed, for I wanted to be a godly husband and father.

Mary finally reached the age when plans for marriage were appropriate, and I spoke to her father. We went through all the customary steps that led to the engagement. The dowry was small, and the betrothal ceremony was simple, but we said our vows with joy. And after the benediction, we drank from the customary cup of wine and received the congratulations of relatives and friends.

Mary and I were bound to each other for life. From that time on I would call her my wife, and she would call me her husband, even though months would pass before we celebrated the wedding feast and began to live together.

During this time, Mary went to visit Elizabeth, her older cousin. I missed her during the three months she was gone. But I knew that she would be a comfort to Elizabeth, who, unbelievably, was pregnant!

After she returned, Mary sent word that she wanted to talk. I greeted her warmly. But I noticed immediately that somehow she was different. There was an aura of dignity and confidence about her. She spoke quietly, and I listened carefully, for I had longed to hear her voice again. But her words just didn't make sense to me. "I'm pregnant," she told me.

I was stunned and heartbroken. I was *not* the baby's father.

"Mary, how did this happen?" I asked in anguish. Then she told me about the visit from the angel and what he had told her. She said she was carrying a child conceived of the Holy Spirit.

I couldn't believe it. How could she have been unfaithful to me? Surely she could not be pregnant and still be a virgin! My mind reeled, and I stumbled away, not knowing or caring where I went.

A war raged within me. My whole conscience had been molded by the Law of Moses, which required a woman who was unfaithful to her husband be stoned to death. But I loved her! In my agony I cried out to God, "What should I do?"

Should I drag my dear Mary into the courtroom and publicly accuse her of adultery? She would not be stoned, for the old law was usually not followed. But she would be exposed to public disgrace and scorn. No, I told myself. I *love her too much to let that happen.*

Or should I divorce her privately and keep the reasons for the divorce to myself? I thought this alternative through carefully. I could just give her the bill of

divorce privately, in the presence of two witnesses, and pay the fine. Then I would quietly say good-bye to her. I would love her always but never see her again.

I wanted to do what was right for Mary. But neither choice was what I really wanted. I sought a reasonable solution, but I was so confused. If only I could believe her story!

As I fell asleep that night, my mind was almost made up. I was inclined to divorce her privately. But then an angel appeared to me in a dream.

"Don't be afraid," the angel told me. "Go through with the marriage feast. Take Mary as your wife. The child she is carrying was conceived of the Holy Spirit."

When I woke up, I didn't know if I should laugh or cry. Mary had told me the truth! So much for reason.

Immediately, I ran to tell her what had happened. I usually didn't have much to say, but that morning my words just tumbled out. Her child would be a boy, the angel had said, and we were to name him Jesus. She cried. So did I, and I asked her to forgive me for not believing her.

Mary and I were married soon. Because of the circumstances, we had a small wedding—just the priest and our families. But that ceremony made Mary's child mine legally. Jesus would be my Son.

During the years that followed, I had time to think about the rest of what the angel had said to me. And Mary and I discussed his words many times.

Why had he addressed me as the son of David? Granted, I was an heir to David's throne, but I would never sit on that throne. Could it be that the angel spoke these words to assure me that one day one of my legal heirs would?

Why did the angel quote from the prophet Isaiah about a virgin conceiving a child, who was "God with us"? Why did the angel reveal to me that Jesus would save His people from their sins? What did these things mean?

Mary and I were never able to understand all of this completely, but this much we knew: Jesus was God in our midst. He was the Savior of the world, and He would reign on the throne of David forever.

I, too, was one of the twelve voices of Christmas. I will never forget the angel's voice—nor the peace and assurance of his words. His message changed not only the course of my life but the destiny of the world.

Gabriel

VOICE OF DISCLOSURE
Luke 1:11-22, 26-38; Matthew 1:20-25

RRG

G abriel's quiet voice disclosed a spectacular message for three central characters in the story of the birth of Jesus. To Zacharias: *Your son will prepare the way for the Messiah.* To Mary: *Your virgin-born Son will be the Messiah, the Son of God.* To Joseph: *Don't be afraid to wed Mary. She will give birth to the Messiah.* These three messages form the heart and the hope of the Christmas story.

I am one of Jehovah's most trusted angels, and He has called on me to deliver many momentous messages. But none can compare with the three I delivered in connection with the birth of the Messiah in Bethlehem—all within months of each other.

The first was to Zacharias. It was a message of good news, but he did not receive it as such.

I remember him as a godly man, an aging priest who served my Master with distinction. His wife, Elizabeth, was also very godly. Both of them were getting up in years, and they had no children. But that was about to change.

Jehovah sent me to tell Zacharias that he and Elizabeth would soon have a son, one who would be filled with the Holy Spirit from Elizabeth's womb. He would be the promised forerunner of the Messiah, in the spirit and power of Elijah.

When the day came, I left the presence of God and flew directly to Jerusalem. It was there, in the temple, that I appeared to Zacharias. He was all alone in the Holy Place, burning incense. In the quiet of that solemn place, I disclosed my message.

"Don't be afraid, Zacharias. Jehovah has heard your prayers, and He is pleased to answer them. You will become a father. Your wife, Elizabeth, will bear a son, and you will name him John."

That should have been cause for celebration. His child was destined to be great in Jehovah's sight. He would turn many people to the Lord. His birth would bring unbounded joy to many people.

But the old priest didn't believe me! He told me that they were too old to have children. I was shocked! I never expected that kind of response.

"I'm Gabriel," I said sternly. "I stand in the presence of God, and I've been sent to you with this news." Surely he would understand that I had direct access to Jehovah and had just come from His throne room with this message.

But he did not believe, and nothing displeases God more than unbelief. "Since you do not believe," I told him, "you will not be able to speak until the day your son is born."

Immediately, I returned to the presence of God, leaving Zacharias to sort out all that had happened to him.

It was just six months later that Jehovah sent me on my second mission. *Perhaps the reception of this message will be different*, I thought.

This time my destination wasn't the capital city or the gleaming temple, but the picturesque village of Nazareth on the southern edge of Galilee. This sleepy little village was a backwater town. People in Israel had little respect for it and would say in derision, "Can anything good come out of Nazareth?"

I was to appear to a young woman named Mary. What I had to tell her was so startling that I knew I must be quiet but strong, and my actions deliberate but gentle. I found her in a humble, little house.

I said, "Be happy, Mary. You are highly favored by God. You are one of the most blessed women on earth."

I could see that my presence troubled her. But it appeared that she was more puzzled by my greeting than she was afraid.

"Don't be afraid, Mary," I continued. "You have found favor with God." I hoped that would calm her. Then I told her she would conceive and bear a Son, and her Son was to be called Jesus.

I had so much more to tell her—that her baby would be great and would be called the Son of the Highest, that Jehovah would give her Son the throne of His father, David, and that there would be no end to His reign.

That's when she interrupted me. She had a puzzled look on her face, and I knew what was bothering her. She wanted to know how she could become pregnant when she was a virgin. It was a fair question.

I'm not sure she fully understood my answer, but I explained that the Holy Spirit would come over her in such a way that she would become pregnant. That meant that the One born would be both God and man. That message contained the most important news, the greatest disclosure, in history.

Mary's response relieved me. She believed! She knew nothing was impossible with God. She calmly and graciously accepted His will for her. How different was her reaction from that of Zacharias.

There was one more message to be delivered, this time to Joseph. Mary was engaged to him. But now she was pregnant, and he deserved to know how it happened. He had to understand that it was both legitimate and acceptable for him to proceed with his marriage plans.

I decided to deliver my message in a dream. I appeared to him suddenly and said, "Joseph, son of David, don't be afraid. Your beloved Mary is pregnant, but she has not been unfaithful to you. What has been conceived in her is from the Holy Spirit of God. She will carry a Son to full term. When He is born, you will take Him as your own Son and name Him Jesus, because He will save His people from their sins."

In the dream I reminded Joseph of what the great prophet said, "Behold, a virgin shall be with child, and bear a Son, and they shall call his name Immanuel." I wanted him to understand that there was no reason for him to file divorce papers on Mary. She had done nothing wrong. While he slept, I quietly slipped away, happy to have been used of God as one of the twelve voices of Christmas.

I told each of these three—Zacharias, Mary and Joseph—"Do not be afraid." These words of comfort were later echoed by the other angels when they appeared to the shepherds. Throughout the ages, men and women who have heard the Christmas story have found that they no longer need to be afraid, for they have come to know the Savior of the world.

Angels

VOICES OF PRAISE
Luke 2:8-14

The heavens echoed with the melody of angels. The glory of the Lord was brilliant and blinding. The audience, a few shepherds, groveled in fear. But they would never forget the message, nor would coming generations forget those words: "There is born to you this day in the city of David a Savior, who is Christ the Lord."

We remember that first Christmas night with crystal clarity. In Bethlehem the inns were full of people who had come for the census. The streets were filled with Roman soldiers, many of whom were drunk. Villagers were carrying on their normal activities. And all were unaware that something spectacular had happened. Jesus, the Savior of the world, had been born.

In the fields outside Bethlehem, some lonely shepherds were watching their flock. Everything was quiet and peaceful.

Then we made our appearance. I appeared first. The glory of the Lord—that heavenly brightness that manifests God's presence and power—lit up the sky like the sun. The shepherds struggled to get to their feet, but they couldn't. So bright was His glory that it pushed them back to their knees. I could see them shaking with fear.

"Don't be afraid," I said. "I bring you good tidings of great joy. For there is born to you this day in the city of David a Savior, who is Christ the Lord."

I told those shepherds that they would find the Savior wrapped in pieces of swaddling cloth and lying in a manger.

Suddenly, I was joined by thousands of my colleagues, angels descending from heaven. Together we said, "Glory to God in the highest, and on earth peace, good will toward men."

The greetings we bore from heaven that night were destined to produce the greatest joy of all time. What greater joy could there be than to know that God had provided a Savior, that He had given a solution to life's greatest problem—the guilt and consequences of sin.

It was a night to praise Jehovah. It was a night to thank the Savior for leaving the glory of heaven to come to earth and assume human flesh. It was a night to thank God for keeping His promise made so long ago in the Garden of Eden.

If we, as angels, had reason to praise God, how much more reason do the people of earth have to praise Him. For they are the ones who need salvation. They are the ones who can rejoice that the Savior has come.

Shepherds

VOICES OF DECLARATION

Luke 2:8-17

RRG

The song of the angels was not heard by priests, Pharisees or rulers, but by lonely, lowly shepherds out in the fields at night. Despised and rejected, they were the first to hear that the Messiah had come. They were the first to see Him, other than Joseph and Mary. And they were the first to declare His coming to other people.

We were usually the last to hear any news, especially good news. We lived isolated lives out in the fields, taking care of our flocks. We minded our own business, and people were happy to leave us alone.

There was a reason for that. We lived outdoors and slept under the stars. We could not possibly keep all the laws, especially the ones the super-spiritual Pharisees had dreamed up. How could we go through all the meticulous hand-washings and other rules and regulations? We were excluded from their religious festivities and considered no better than thieves. We were the most despised class of people in Israel.

It did not matter to them what we felt in our hearts. We prayed during our lonely watches and often talked about God. We longed to see the Messiah, and we longed for His coming.

In these pastures, their ancestor David had fought the lion and bear to protect his sheep. We were protecting the lambs that would be offered as sacrifices for their sin in the temple. But that meant nothing to them.

A shepherd doesn't have much excitement in his life. It's lonely and sometimes dull. Our days were spent hunting for what little grass we could find and caring for the animals. In the evening we generally bedded down with the sheep under a tree or led them to some crude shelter—a pen or a sheepfold. We took turns at night watching them to make sure they were not devoured by wild animals.

But on one starlit night, while we were resting in the cool of the evening, a figure appeared out of nowhere. We didn't know who he was or where he came from. Suddenly, it became piercingly bright all around us. We fell to the ground in fear.

We'd heard about the Shekinah glory. We knew the stories of Moses at the burning bush and the pillar of fire in the desert. This had to be the glory of the Lord! This figure before us was not another shepherd; it was an angel sent from God.

We were frightened out of our minds. I remember covering my head and my eyes. I thought I might die. Then I heard the angel speak. "Don't be afraid," he said. I felt a calmness, and a quiet awe came over me. He was not going to bring any judgment on us. He was going to give us some kind of news—good news.

"There is born to you this day in Bethlehem a Savior, who is Christ the Lord." I felt a joy I had never experienced before. The Messiah had been born—the one for whom our people had waited so long! This was the fulfillment of centuries of hope and prayer.

Suddenly, the angel was joined by an army of angels. They were coming from everywhere, and the sky was filled with them. They began to praise God, saying, "Glory to God in the highest, and on earth peace, good will toward men!" I'd never heard rolling thunder louder than their booming voices. We were astonished!

When their hymn ended, we saw them ascending to heaven. The light faded out of the sky, and we were left alone. But their message remained with us.

When we found our voices, we could speak of only one thing. We must go to Bethlehem to see the baby. The angel had taken it for granted that we would go. He had even told us how to identify Him. He would be in a manger, wrapped in swaddling cloth. We did not question. We did not hesitate. We went.

As we traveled, I kept thinking to myself, *That's not where the Messiah should be, in a manger, wrapped in strips of cloth. He should be in the king's palace or maybe at the temple itself, wrapped in purple.*

At last we found the place where Mary, the mother of the baby, and her husband, Joseph, were. We found them in the poorest and most humble of circumstances. What a contrast with the splendor of the announcement of His birth! But we were not put off, for we knew who this baby was.

I can still remember the look on Joseph's face when we approached. Why were we there? Why were we intruding when he and his wife wanted some privacy? Looking beyond him, we saw Mary, gazing with wonder at the baby in the manger; and we fell on our knees and worshipped Him.

Finally, I told Joseph the whole story about the angels and their message. "We had to come and see for ourselves," I told him. "We wanted to praise Him too."

As I was standing there, amazed and filled with awe, a story came to my mind. I thought of what had happened to the four lepers of Samaria years ago.

SHEPHERDS, VOICES OF DECLARATION

The Syrians had been menacing our people, and there was a great famine. Four lepers decided to give themselves up to the Syrians to get some food. When they arrived at the enemy camp, they found it empty. All the Syrians were gone. They went from tent to tent and found food, water, clothes—everything they could want.

That discovery saved their lives. One of them said, "This is a day of good news, and we cannot remain silent." So they determined to tell the people in the besieged city.

That's exactly how my friends and I felt. After we had worshipped the Christ child, we left the cattle stall. "This is good news," we told each other. "People need to hear that the Savior has been born." So that night we joined the twelve voices of Christmas as the voices of declaration. We told everyone we met about the birth of the Christ-child.

After that night I often thought about what the angel had said, "There is born to *you* this day a Savior." Born to *us*? To shepherds? Why had God honored us and not the priests, the scribes and royalty?

To me it was ironic that those uppity Pharisees in Jerusalem, who had studied the Law and kept all the commandments, were not the first ones to hear the news they had waited so long to hear. Neither were they the first ones to see the newborn Messiah. We were the first to see Him—lonely, lowly shepherds. I guess when God has a task as important as telling the world about the Savior, He doesn't entrust it to those who worship Him out of habit but to those who worship Him out of love.

Simeon

VOICE OF PEACE
Luke 2:25-35

imeon, who longed for peace, found it in the form of a baby— God's promised Prince of Peace. Having seen this child, the salvation of God, he rejoiced that he could now die in peace. In an outburst of praise, he prophesied that this salvation would extend to all peoples of the world.

I was so tired that I wanted to die. My country was in chaos, and my people were steeped in sin and rebellion against the Lord. I longed for righteousness and—most of all—peace.

We were a conquered country, subject to the Romans. Sixty years before, when General Pompeii marched in and subdued our land, we knew that we had fallen to a sophisticated military power. The Romans became entrenched in our country. They set up camps, built fortresses and dug artificial harbors. No one liked them. We didn't want them here, but it was evident that they intended to stay.

Surprisingly, in many ways they treated us with respect. They allowed us to continue to practice our religion and to build synagogues. We were exempt from service in the Roman army, and they did not force us to violate our Sabbath. On the other hand, they confiscated our homes, violated our women and demoralized our nation. There was no peace in our land, and there wouldn't be as long as the Romans were there.

But I hadn't lost hope. In the midst of all the darkness, degradation and despair, there was a small group of us, men and women, earnestly anticipating a day when Israel would be free from the Romans. God had promised to bring blessing, comfort, joy and peace to us in the Person of the Messiah. Our oppression intensified our longing for the One who would deliver us. We called this "waiting for the consolation of Israel."

I was just an ordinary man, not a priest, not even a Levite. I had no place of importance, either to the temple or to my nation. But I was honest in my dealings with others and conscientious in carrying out the duties God had assigned me.

My sorrow for my nation was so deep and so painful that I made a special request to God. "Please, don't let my eyes close in death until I have seen the promised Messiah. Please let me see the salvation of Israel." The Holy Spirit then gave me a significant promise: You will not die until you see Him.

One day I felt drawn to go to the temple. I hadn't planned to be there that day, but I soon found myself walking through its courts.

While I was there, one particular young couple with a baby caught my attention. I started walking toward them. Obviously they were there for the mother's purification and the child's presentation. It was common to see parents bring their babies there for that purpose.

Suddenly I knew—somehow I just knew—this baby was the Messiah. Only the Spirit of God could have revealed this to me.

I looked the young mother in the eye and asked, "Dear sister, would you let me hold your child?" After a quick glance toward the man and an affirming nod from him, she looked at me and gently handed me her baby. I took Him in my arms and held Him close to my chest. My eyes filled with tears.

I then held Him with both hands, high in the air, and began to praise God. "Lord, now You are letting Your servant depart in peace, according to Your word; for my eyes have seen Your salvation."

Until that day I had felt like a servant who had been told by his master to go to a high place and watch for the appearance of a special star. I had watched through long, wearisome hours during the dark night, and now, finally, I had seen the star.

I knew that this baby was the salvation of God. And in the midst of my praise, God showed me something new. His light, His salvation, would shine beyond the Jewish nation in its present oppression. His light would shine so brightly that all nations would see it.

When I finished praying, my beard was wet with my tears. I handed the infant back to His mother. Both parents looked amazed. Perhaps they were surprised and delighted that God had revealed this secret to me. Perhaps it was because my words of praise had given them a clearer understanding of the divine majesty of their baby.

They introduced themselves as Joseph and Mary, and their baby was named Jesus. They told me about the message of the angel to Mary concerning the conception of the child. They told me of the assurance an angel had given Joseph. They told me about Jesus' birth in Bethlehem and about the shepherds who came to worship Him. They told about the angel's message to the shepherds—the announcement that Jesus had been born in Bethlehem.

We had been speaking of glorious things. But God then gave me a message for the couple, which gave another side of the picture. The salvation this child would bring would be purchased at a high cost. He would bring out all the evil concealed in the hearts of wicked men. And Mary would have her heart pierced again and again by the sorrows she would witness and experience. This child, Jesus, was to be a stumbling block to some, but a stepping stone to others.

I had looked for peace—in life and as I looked toward death. I did not live in a peaceful land, nor in a peaceful time in history. Still, I could be one of the twelve voices of Christmas—the voice of peace— for on that wonderful day in the temple, I held the only One who could bring real peace to the world. At last, after seeing Him, I was ready to die in peace.

Anna

VOICE OF THANKSGIVING
Luke 2:36-38

Anna's people were oppressed and burdened, but she was not discouraged. Any day now God would send the Redeemer He had promised, and she would see Him. One day, as she was praying in the temple, she looked across the courtyard and saw Him—just a baby. And suddenly she knew He was the Promised One. With her spirit soaring, she lifted up her voice in praise and thanksgiving.

The Lord took my husband from me when we had been married for only seven years. But in exchange, He gave me Himself. I was 84 when this story began, and during all the years of my widowhood, God had been much more to me than a husband.

In my sorrow I fled to Him, and He comforted me. In response, I decided to give my whole attention to Him and His work, not to myself. So I dedicated myself to Him—in prayer, in praise and in fasting.

The temple was my constant and most loved resort. I was there daily and never missed a service. I kept all the customary fasts and additional fasts as God led me. I spent hours in prayer each day. God gave me strength beyond my years, and I used that strength in thankful praise to Him.

I was not lonely. People who frequented the temple were familiar with my face and my dedication to my Lord. Among them God had given me friends who had the same kind of joy and expectation I had; they were almost like family. Each of us was scaling a pinnacle of hope and expectation.

We were living in dreadful times. We saw the moral and religious decay in Jerusalem and in our country. Even in the temple we were surrounded by corruption. People had lost hope, and a sense of darkness and gloom overshadowed their lives.

We earnestly longed for deliverance. *Surely*, we thought, *the redemption God had promised was near! Surely the Messiah would come soon!* That expectation put a spring in my step and a radiance in my life.

We had to be very circumspect when we greeted each other or met together, however. This was, after all, a land ruled by Herod. If he had known we were talking about a coming Messiah, about liberation from his rule, he would have silenced us quickly.

Then one day, while I was in the temple, the most wonderful event of my life took place.

I was standing in the courtyard praying. People were coming and going as they always did. I happened to look up, and across the courtyard I could see a man and his young wife enter the temple carrying a little baby.

No sooner had they entered the courtyard than an old man approached them. I could see them talking, but at first I couldn't hear what they were saying. I noticed the pretty wife look at her husband and then look back at the old man and offer her baby to him. He took the child in his arms and then held him above his head.

He raised his voice, and from across the courtyard I could hear him praising God. I couldn't catch everything he said, but he did mention something about peace and about seeing God's salvation.

I walked through the portico and up the stairs to the level of the courtyard where the couple stood. I approached quietly and cautiously. By then the old man had finished his prayer and had handed the baby back to the mother. He was talking to her, more quietly, so I couldn't hear what he said. But I could see a look of concern come over the her face.

There was something different about this child—I just knew it. God had given me supernatural insight at other times, and I sensed that this was happening again. That awareness, plus the

unusual behavior and words of this man, came together in my mind in a burst of understanding. This baby *was* God's salvation! He *was* the Messiah!

When I arrived where the couple stood, the old man had just finished his conversation with the mother. Without pause, I raised my hands in prayer, giving thanks to God for bringing this baby into the world.

What a celebration it became! Then I introduced myself. "My name is Anna, the daughter of Phanuel of the tribe of Asher." When I told them I was a prophetess, the couple looked surprised, though they understood what that meant. On certain occasions God had divinely inspired me, by the power of His Spirit, to speak His word to others, to make His will known.

It had been many years since the voice of prophecy had been heard in our land. God had been silent. In fact, we had heard no great prophets since the days of Malachi, hundreds of years before. This young couple was probably astounded to learn that prophecy was again being heard in our land.

I am sure they understood the import of my voice of thanksgiving and praise that day. When I had seen that child, God had opened my eyes. This was the Messiah! I didn't understand everything about Him, but I knew He was the key to our redemption. My words were a doxology to the Father, who had sent Him, the One who fulfills His promises.

After the couple left, I stood in silence. I had looked for and longed for the coming of this promised Redeemer for so long. And now He was here. I was an old woman, but the sight of that baby had given me renewed strength and courage to go on. I would tell about Him for the rest of my days.

I was eager to tell my friends, the ones who earnestly hoped for His coming. I spoke first to a godly woman who often prayed in the temple. "Praise God!" I said. "The Messiah is here. I have seen Him with my own eyes." She looked at me in wonderment. Then I told her the whole story, and relief and joy came over her. When she left, she seemed to be walking on air. Others reacted the same way. Soon a wide circle of people knew that Messiah had come.

I don't remember everything I said as one of the twelve voices of Christmas, but I do remember repeating many poems of praise from the great singers of Israel.

"Let us come before His presence with thanksgiving; let us shout joyfully to Him with psalms" (Ps. 95:2).

"Enter into His gates with thanksgiving, and into His courts with praise. Be thankful to Him, and bless his name" (Ps. 100:4).

"I will praise the name of God with a song, and will magnify Him with thanksgiving" (Ps. 69:30).

"I will offer to You the sacrifice of thanksgiving, and will call upon the name of the Lord" (Ps. 116:17).

God gave me the great honor and privilege of being the first one to proclaim the Redeemer. My faith was at last changed to sight, and my hope was turned to certainty. The waning years of my life were devoted to praise and thanksgiving.

Wise Men

Voices of Adoration
Matthew 2:1-12

RRG

The Wise Men traveled hundreds of miles and diligently searched for the child-king. And when they found Him, they offered their gifts and adoration. They recognized that He was not only the Jewish Messiah, the anointed One of Israel, but also the Savior of the world. Through the ages, their story and example have challenged millions to adore Him as Christ the Lord.

I still remember seeing the dirt floor of that primitive house. Early in my academic training, I never would have guessed that I'd be in such a situation. My friends and I had traveled hundreds of miles—not to see a potentate or an intellectual, but a baby! And at the end of our journey, my face was almost on the ground. I saw nothing but dirt.

Who were we? Some people called us wise men. Actually, we were Babylonians, part of a caste of men who were appointed to the court in Babylon. As the most learned men of our country, we had dedicated our lives to the study of the sciences, especially astronomy. Our knowledge was kind of an alchemy of science and superstition. Some called us astrologers, because we studied the constellations and their effects on society. Some also had dabbled a bit in the black arts—divination, magic, sorcery, that sort of thing.

But we were not unique in the history of Israel. Jewish people had encountered our kind before. Joseph met wise men in Egypt, as did the great leader Moses. One of the great heroines, Esther, had contact with them in the Persian Empire. Even the great Jewish prophets, like Jeremiah and Ezekiel, spoke of wise men. But we were different from all of those other wise men. We were searching for the Jewish Messiah.

The story of how we got to that house in Bethlehem and on our faces before the young child was filled with adventure, danger and intrigue. We were not kings, as some may have thought; we came to Judea in *search* of a King. We had come for one reason, and one reason only—to worship Him and to raise our voices in adoration.

How did we learn about Him? We knew that the Jewish nation expected a Messiah, who would bring peace and freedom, joy and comfort, and salvation to all mankind. Perhaps our people learned this from Jewish wise men, such as Daniel, Hananiah, Mishael and Azariah, when they were in captivity in our nation. This information had been passed down from one generation of wise men to another.

Though we were of Babylonian blood, we were eager to meet someone like that promised Messiah. And we fell on our faces before Him when we saw Him. In the presence of such deity and glory, any intelligent person would do the same.

How did we know that we should search for Him? As we were watching the heavens, we saw a special star rising in the east. It had to be an indication from the God of heaven that He was about to fulfill His promise. So we set out on our journey westward. The star did not go with us, nor did it lead us. In fact, it disappeared, and we didn't see it again until later, when we left Jerusalem.

Once in Jerusalem, we began to inquire where the One who was born King of the Jews might be. We were surprised when no one seemed to know. We had come hundreds of miles to see the child-king, but they didn't even know there *was* a child-king. Perhaps we had come for no reason at all.

Our first big break came when the ruler, a man named Herod, called us to his palace. We thought it strange that he summoned us at night. It appeared that he didn't want anyone to know we were even there. Herod seemed very interested in this child. He told us to look in Bethlehem and commanded us to go there, find the child and return to him so that he, too, could worship Him.

While Herod appeared very sincere in his desire to worship the anointed One, we found out later that he was a deceiver. He wanted to kill the child!

Unaware of Herod's intent, we set out from Jerusalem to go to Bethlehem. It was only when we saw the star again that we knew for sure we had a reliable guide to the King.

The star hung low in the heavens, and it led us right to the Bethlehem house where Mary, Joseph and the young boy were living. We knocked at the door, and Mary answered. Again we posed the question we had asked so frequently in Jerusalem, "Where is He who has been born King of the Jews?" The stunned look on Mary's face clearly told us she was uneasy about our being there. Likely she had assumed that the excitement about her baby's birth had now waned and she and her family could expect to live normal lives. But there we were, strangers from the East dressed in elegant Babylonian gowns.

Then her husband appeared at the door. He quizzed us about who we were and what our intentions were. Satisfied with our answers, the couple graciously invited us into their cramped quarters—probably part of a relative's house, because Mary and Joseph told us they were not permanent residents of Bethlehem.

When we saw the child, we fell to the floor on our faces. The star had led us to the house, but more importantly, to the One whom we would later understand was not just the Jewish Messiah, but the incarnate God, the Savior of the world.

Then we lifted our heads and raised our voices in adoration to the King. We also presented our treasure chests of gifts to Him.

I brought gold because it was the most precious commodity in our world. It represented royalty and should be associated with kings, queens and princes. I presented gold to the child, as my King.

My friend presented frankincense. It was grown in southern Arabia and East Africa, and it was precious to everyone. To us it represented service to Jehovah and was given as an act of worship and adoration to this child by servants of Jehovah.

Another friend brought myrrh, sometimes used as an anointing oil. To us it spoke of the pleasant perfumes with which bodies were embalmed. Although we did not know everthing about the child-king at the time, we learned the rest of the story in eternity. What a fitting gift! For while this child had just begun His life, a sacrificial death was to be His destiny.

We presented ourselves in adoration to Jesus as we gave these gifts. We understood Him to be much more than a baby born in humble circumstances in Bethlehem. We learned that He was God in the flesh—God with us.

VOICE OF DECEPTION
Matthew 2:1-12

HEROD, VOICE OF DECEPTION

Herod's was the voice of deception. He had no intention of worshipping a "pretender" to his throne. He wanted only to kill Him. In the great carol of Christmas, he was the singer in the minor key, clashing with the pure melody sung by the other singers. He will always be remembered as the voice no one wanted to hear.

Had you entered my presence, you would have bowed. I was known as Herod the Great, king of the Jews. I was the most powerful man in my part of the world, and I knew everything that went on in my region. I was in complete control.

People said bad things about me. It's true that I was ruthless. I drank heavily and was prone to outbursts of violence. But I was a cunning negotiator and a superb diplomat. I subdued the opposition and maintained order among the Jewish people for nearly 33 years. The emperor and all the powerful people in Rome were pleased with my reign.

Everything I did was absolutely necessary. I was the best thing that had ever happened to those Jews. They criticized me because I killed all my brothers and half-brothers, who could have challenged my reign, but I would do it again in a minute. I would have done anything to maintain my position as king of the Jews. I even murdered my wife, Mariamne. It was a shame too—she was my favorite. I had ten marriages and fathered 15 children. None of them pleased me.

When Mariamne's two sons, Alexander and Aristobulus, realized I had killed their mother, I had to murder them as well. I can still hear those ungrateful Jews quip, "It's better to be Herod's hog than to be his son."

Why did people keep dwelling on these negative things? Didn't they know how much I did for them and that wretched land? I built cities and fortresses. I protected them from invaders. I introduced them to Greek literature, art and athletic contests. And for years I was involved in rebuilding the Jewish temple in Jerusalem. I left behind me roads and buildings and culture that they never could have dreamed of without me.

I did all that for those people, and they didn't appreciate me one bit. All they remembered was the bloodshed. They talked about my deception and ruthlessness. They said I was cruel, cold-blooded and brutal.

I really didn't want to deceive those travelers from the East, but it angered me when they asked, "Where is the One who has been born King of the Jews?" What did they mean by that? I was the king of the Jews!

Jerusalem was a metropolitan city. We had visitors all the time, from the east, the west, from Africa, from all over. But some men had come from the east, I had heard, looking for a child they said was born King of the Jews. According to reports, they were saying something about coming to Judea to find Him, because they had seen His star rise in the east. I didn't remember seeing any star. But if they wanted to know, they should have come straight to me.

When that news reached me, I was frightened. So was everyone else in Jerusalem. They didn't want any more trouble stirred up, nor any more blood spilled. They knew I was determined to keep my throne. As long as I lived, only I would be king of the Jews. It had taken years of struggle to get where I was, and I wasn't going to give all this up to some baby.

I also didn't want such rumors to stir up the fanatics, who hated me. They would attempt an insurrection for sure, because they always wanted to rid their land of the Romans. I had to get to the bottom of this immediately.

My first thought was to get more information from the Jews, so I called in their chief priests and scribes and asked them if there was any truth to a prophecy that a Messiah would be born.

They said there was and that their prophet Micah had identified the village of Bethlehem in Judah as His birthplace. That was hitting too close to home. I knew I had to act quickly. I dismissed the Jews and had my aides set up a clandestine meeting with the Babylonians. Everyone called them wise men—I was going to see how wise they were.

I would ask them when they had seen His star rise. That would tell me how long ago this baby had been born. (I wouldn't tell them what my real intention was.) Then I would order them to go to Bethlehem and find the young child and return to tell me, so I could worship Him.

I had no intention of worshipping this pretender to my throne. I wanted only to kill Him. If members of my own family had become expendable because they stood in my way, did the Jews think for one minute I wouldn't take the life of a little Jewish baby?

At the appointed hour they arrived at my palace. I found them to be more cooperative than I had expected, and they willingly pinpointed the time when they had first seen the star. I commanded them to go to Bethlehem, find the child and return here. My plan worked perfectly. When they returned, I would simply send a contingent of soldiers to kill the baby. That would be the end of that.

Well, I waited for these wise men to return to my palace. It must have been for about a week. I was nervous the whole time. Had they found the baby? Was He really the expected Messiah the Jews looked for? Could He really be a threat to my reign? The wise men held the answers to all these questions. Where were they? Why weren't they back? I waited.

Eventually I realized that they weren't coming. I had deceived them. Now they had deceived me and had apparently returned to Babylon without my knowledge. I had to take matters into my own hands.

I sent soldiers to Bethlehem with orders to put to death every male child two years and younger. I knew they were innocent children, but what did I care? I did what I had to do. I was merely protecting my throne.

I learned later that in Jerusalem the whisperers called this the slaughter of the innocents. They called this the most diabolical move of my regency. When people thought of me, they remembered only my deception and the killing of these innocent children—not the buildings I had erected, not the harbors I had dug, not the cultural and educational benefits I had brought to that land.

They didn't understand. I couldn't let a baby be a threat to me. It was hard enough keeping the Jews in line. If they had thought they had a champion, if they had thought their long-awaited Messiah had come, there would have been even more bloodshed.

John

VOICE OF PREPARATION
Luke 1:13-17

JOHN, VOICE OF PREPARATION

ike a prelude to a symphony, John's voice rose in the desert, saying, "Messiah is coming. Prepare for Him." Later, his call to repentance softened and faded into the background as the One who was born in Bethlehem as the Savior of the world began His public ministry.

As far back as I can remember, I knew I was different. As I grew up, the differences between me and people around me became more pronounced.

I asked my father why. He was a very godly priest, and I thought he could help me through those difficult times. In answer, he told me the story of my birth.

My birth was a miracle, he said. He and my mother had prayed for a son for many years, but were childless. Finally they had given up hope, for they were too old to have a baby.

Then one day when my father was serving in the sanctuary of the temple, an angel appeared to him and told him that he and my mother were to have a son. I would be a very special son, the angel told him. I would be filled with the Holy Spirit from my mother's womb. That's why I was different, my father said.

That was about all I could take for one day. So he told me the rest of the story, bit by bit, as I grew older. I was to be the voice of preparation—I had been chosen by God to prepare the way for the Messiah, and I was to serve as His forerunner, in the spirit and power of the prophet Elijah.

Malachi, one of our famous prophets, had even spoken of the messenger who would pave the way for the Messiah. The prophet Isaiah had referred to him as a voice crying in the wilderness. "That's who you are and what you are to do," my father told me.

It wasn't until I was grown and had retreated to the wilderness that I had enough solitude and time to think through everything my parents had experienced and everything the angel had told my father. I lived simply, wearing a garment made of camel's hair with a leather girdle, and eating only locusts and wild honey.

There, in my solitude, I communed with God's Spirit, until I fully understood His call and commission to me. I knew that Messiah was alive, but I did not know who He was. I understood the corruption in men's hearts and the terrible judgment awaiting them if they did not repent. And I was certain that the Holy Spirit was driving me to preach this message: "Repent, for the kingdom of heaven is at hand."

John, Voice of Preparation

So I left my solitary life and began preaching in the area of the Jordan River. Multitudes came to listen—peasants from Jerusalem and as far away as Galilee, soldiers on their way from Damascus to Petra, even priests and scribes from Jerusalem. They came to hear me speak and to watch me baptize in the river. Some were just curious. Some laughed at the way I dressed. Some thought I was Elijah resurrected.

I was not an eloquent or polished speaker. My preaching would probably be described as fiery and bombastic, and I always spoke of the inevitable and impending judgment of God. But with my whole heart I wanted my listeners to escape that judgment, so I tirelessly pointed out the way to safety. "Repent!" I told them. "Forsake your sin. The Messiah is coming. Be ready for Him."

Isaiah had prophesied that I was to make Messiah's paths straight. What a picture! In days past, before a king went on a journey, he sometimes sent a courier ahead to tell people to prepare for his coming. They were commanded to straighten out the winding paths and smooth out the rocky ones.

I was like that courier, telling people they should be prepared to receive the Messiah. And I told them they needed to correct the moral obstacles in their lives.

My baptism appealed to many people who weren't really interested in my message of repentance. They wanted some magical rite performed on them by someone they considered a prophet. But I told them, "You can't escape punishment this way! You are hypocrites. You come to me like a brood of vipers who scurry out of their hiding places to escape the flames when dry brushwood and stubble catch fire."

I reminded them of the judgment to come, when the truly repentant would be separated from the unrepentant, just as the good grain is separated from the chaff on the threshing floor. They would suffer punishment, just as certainly as the chaff is burned.

For the most part, people weren't prepared for my message of repentance. But then, people are rarely prepared to hear what they need to hear.

I had upset both the religious and the political establishments. I once blasted Herod the Tetrarch for divorcing his wife and marrying his brother's wife, Herodias. Later I was captured by him, held in a dungeon and eventually beheaded. Even if I had known that, it would have made no difference. I would not have backed down.

Not too far into my ministry it was rumored that I was the Messiah.

I made it quite clear that I was not by showing them two ways in which we were different. "He is greater than I am," I said, "so great that I am not worthy enough even to untie His sandals." I also told them, "I baptize with water, but He will baptize with the Holy Spirit." I was using a physical object—water. His work would be spiritual. He would have the power to purify hearts and give eternal life.

At that time I still did not know who the Messiah was. Then one day a relative of mine, Jesus, came from Galilee to the Jordan and asked me to baptize Him. I knew something of the purity of His life, so at first I refused. I told Him that I needed to be baptized by Him. But Jesus said that it was fitting for us to fulfill all righteousness.

When He came out of the water, I saw the heavens open, and the Spirit of God descended like a dove and alighted on Him. And I heard a voice from heaven: "This is My beloved Son, in whom I am well pleased."

Then I knew that Jesus was the Messiah! I reflected on the stories from my youth—of the supernatural conception of Jesus, of the promises of prophets and angels, of my miraculous conception six months before Mary conceived Jesus, and of my leap within my mother's womb in recognition that Mary carried the Anointed One of Israel.

I had not been present at the birth of Jesus; and even if I had, I would have been too young to understand what was happening. But I was a vital part of that marvelous, majestic story.

In Jehovah's eternal plan, my task was to point men to Jesus. When He began His public ministry, I realized that He must increase, and I must decrease. After all, I was a herald, and of what use is a herald after the king has arrived?

My call to repentance softened, and I faded into the background. Yet I continued to point to Jesus as the expected Messiah.